Check, Please!

A To-Do Journal for Educators

Tangular A. Irby

Nikki, Thank you for accepting this. I hot have me to you.

https://tangularirby.com/
Photography by Dawn Langston

Dedication

This journal is dedicated to new beginnings and dreams that never die.

Love,

Ms Irby

Introduction

During the pandemic and a power outage, I rediscovered the power of physically writing my daily to-do list. At that point, I was jotting my lists on scraps of paper or large sticky notes. Actually, whatever was available became fair game. My written plan became a tangible contract between my thoughts and my actions. Each day, I would create a list, complete the tasks, discard my accomplishments and repeat. What if all my tasks and lists could be preserved for future reference?

Have you ever lost your to-do list and couldn't move forward until you recreated it? This simple "to-do" journal will rid you of keeping track of individual scraps of paper and allow you to record your activity in one place. Fill in the heading with today's date, the month, or a special assignment or project. It is completely up to you! Check the heading when you have accomplished every task on the page!

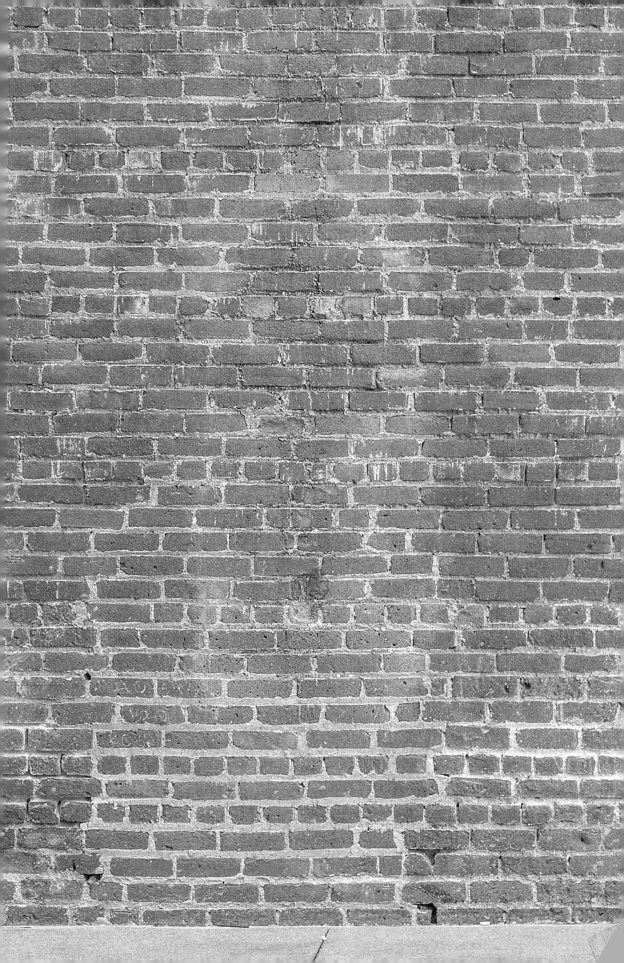

Unclutter ∽ Strategize ∽ Check

Unclutter ∽ Strategize ∽ Check

Unclutter ∽ Strategize ∽ Check

Unclutter ∿ Strategize ∿ Check

Unclutter ∽ **Strategize** ∽ **Check**

Unclutter ∿ Strategize ∿ Check

Unclutter ⌇Strategize⌇ Check

Unclutter ∽Strategize∽ Check

Unclutter ～**Strategize**～ **Check**

Unclutter ∽**Strategize**∽ **Check**

Unclutter ∿**Strategize**∿ **Check**

Unclutter ∿ **Strategize** ∿ **Check**

Unclutter ∿ Strategize ∿ Check

Unclutter ∽ Strategize ∽ Check

Unclutter ～Strategize～ Check

Unclutter ∽ **Strategize** ∽ **Check**

Unclutter ∿ **Strategize** ∿ **Check**

Unclutter ∾ **Strategize** ∾ **Check**

Unclutter ∿ Strategize∿ Check

Unclutter ∿Strategize∿ Check

☐ _____

☐

☐

☐

☐

☐

☐

☐

☐

☐

☐

☐

☐

Unclutter ∾ Strategize ∾ Check

Unclutter ∽**Strategize**∽ **Check**

Unclutter ◡ Strategize ◡ Check

Unclutter ∼◦Strategize∼◦ **Check**

Unclutter ~Strategize~ Check

☐ _____

☐

☐

☐

☐

☐

☐

☐

☐

☐

☐

☐

☐

Unclutter ∾ Strategize ∾ Check

Unclutter ⌇**Strategize**⌇ **Check**

Unclutter ∾Strategize∾ Check

Unclutter ∽**Strategize**∽ **Check**

☐ _____

☐

☐

☐

☐

☐

☐

☐

☐

☐

☐

☐

Unclutter ∾ Strategize ∾ Check

Unclutter ～**Strategize**～ **Check**

Unclutter ~ **Strategize** ~ **Check**

Unclutter ∽**Strategize**∽ **Check**

Unclutter ∽ **Strategize** ∽ **Check**

Unclutter ～**Strategize**～ **Check**

Unclutter ～**Strategize**～ **Check**

Unclutter ∿Strategize∿ Check

Unclutter ∿Strategize∿ Check

Unclutter ∽ Strategize ∽ Check

Unclutter ～**Strategize**～ **Check**

Unclutter ∿ **Strategize** ∿ **Check**

Unclutter ∽ Strategize ∽ Check

Unclutter ∽ **Strategize** ∽ **Check**

Unclutter ∿**Strategize**∿ **Check**

Unclutter ∼ **Strategize** ∼ **Check**

Unclutter ∽Strategize∽ Check

Unclutter ～**Strategize**～ **Check**

Unclutter ∽ Strategize ∽ Check

Unclutter ∾ **Strategize** ∾ **Check**

Unclutter ∽**Strategize** ∽ **Check**

Unclutter ∼°**Strategize**∼° **Check**

Unclutter ∿**Strategize**∿ **Check**

Unclutter ～**Strategize**～ **Check**

Unclutter ∿ Strategize ∿ Check

Unclutter ∼ **Strategize** ∼ **Check**

Unclutter ∾Strategize∾ Check

Unclutter ∽**Strategize**∽ **Check**

Unclutter ∿ **Strategize** ∿ **Check**

Unclutter ∽**Strategize**∽ **Check**

Unclutter ∾ **Strategize** ∾ **Check**

Unclutter ∾**Strategize**∾ **Check**

Unclutter ∿Strategize∿ Check

Unclutter ～ **Strategize** ～ **Check**

Unclutter ∽ Strategize ∽ Check

Unclutter ∾ Strategize ∾ Check

Unclutter ∿ **Strategize** ∿ **Check**

Made in the USA
Middletown, DE
11 May 2021